Real letters from
real students!

Inquiries should be addressed to hello@scottgrizzly.com.

All of the student writing compiled in this book was written by fourth graders from the western United States.

www.scottgrizzlysorensen.com

Dear Mr. Mountain Man

Letters to Scott Grizzly Sorensen

Howdy Partners,

Since I left my lodge in the north woods of Canada last fall, I've been out on the trail swapping yarns and tall tales about mountain men. They were the heroes of the American west and renowned storytellers. Nothing satisfies the soul like a good story.

In my travels to schools across the country I have met some natural-born storytellers. And most of them are ten-year-olds. They speak their minds and shoot straight from the hip. Every school has its characters, both rascals and angels. Their voices are heard in the following letters, so hold on to your hats and enjoy the ride.

Your friend,
Grizzly

Dear Mr. Mountain Man,

I liked your funny stories. I didn't hear a lot of them because my teacher, "Mrs. Dork," accidentally forgot about the assembly, so I only saw the last 20 minutes. I thought it was a blast! Especially the gun shot. BANG! It nearly Killed my ears. But it sure was fun.

Sincerely,

Kristina

p.s. Your tall tales and HawKen rifle really expired me.

Dear Kristina,

I am amazed that "Mrs. Dork" is still teaching. I had her in the fourth grade too. And you're not the first person to be expired by a Hawken rifle. It happened all the time in the old days when mountain men fought battles with their enemies.

In fact, Mrs. Dork asked me to come back to your school next year and expire some more fourth graders.

Your friend,
Griz

Hi Mountain Man,

My name is Bucky and my story is this: One day my dad shot a coyote in our field and put it in the freezer. He was going to skin it, but he left it there for three years. My mom didn't like it and threw it in the garbage. But my dad found it and put it back in the freezer. Anyway, for their anniversary they went on a trip to a hotel and gave each other presents. My mom got some flowers and a pearl necklace. My dad got the frozen coyote.

That is my story.

Your friend,

Bucky

Dear Bucky,

That is the most romantic story I have ever heard. When I read your letter to my wife, Mrs. Grizzly, there were tears in her eyes. I have never seen a letter affect a woman like that.

I told her that I would have put a coyote in the freezer years ago if I had known how it would make her feel. I am going to surprise her with a big badger that got hit on the canyon road yesterday. I will hide it behind the frozen turkey on the bottom shelf. It will be a Thanksgiving surprise!

Thanks for the good idea,
Grizzly

Dear Mountain Man,

Lots of Kids in my class think you are like a homeless person. But I think you are just like us. You probably have a television and a game boy.

School is very boring. All we do is sit in class listening to our teacher. It is like watching a tree sloth.

I am 10 years old and I like to fish and hunt and be outdoors. But my dad is a pastor. That's about all I have to say. Except, you are the best mountain man I have ever seen. Actually, you are the only mountain man I have ever seen.

Your friend,

Emmit

p.s. I don't mean to be rude, but when you die can I have your rifle, traps and animal furs?

Dear Emmit,

Mountain men were kind of like homeless people. They wandered from place to place looking for food and shelter. The mountains and deserts were their floors and walls, and the moon and stars were their roof at night.

John "Liver-eating" Johnson was one of those wild and woolly mountain men. When he was seventy years old, a news reporter asked him if he'd ever had an Indian wife.

"Certainly," replied Johnson, "but I sent her to Rome."

"To Rome, Italy?"

"No. To roam on the prairie," roared Johnson.

Ha ha! Get it, Emmit? Roam on the prairie!

Keep your powder dry,

Grizzly

Hey Grizzly,

It was sure fun to see you again in the fourth grade this year.

I saw you last year in the fourth grade too and I told my teacher that I wanted to see you next year in the fifth grade, but she said, "No! It is only for fourth graders." Anyway, I got held back. Which just goes to show that teachers don't know everything.

Have a fine day, Mountain Man. I will probably see you again next year.

Your biggest fan,

Zachary

p.s. Write back soon but not in cursive please.

Hello, Zachary,

I'm mighty pleased that you enjoy my program so much. See you next year!

Grizzly

Dear Mr. Mountain Man,

I loved your stories about trappers like Kit Carson and Jim Bridger eating buffaloes, bears, and beaver tails. It sounded so good.

My mom is a vegetarian. That is a person who just cooks vegetables. I get so sick of barbecued zucchinis and soybean burgers.

It was so fun when my mom went on a trip. Every night me and Dad ate steaks, chicken, pork chops, and buffalo wings which are not actually from buffaloes. They are chicken wings with buffalo sauce on them. We even went to Carl's Jr. and got a triple bacon burger with cheese and extra bacon. It was the best week ever!

I'll give you some advice Mountain Man. Don't be a vegetarian. You would hate it.

Your friend,

Jessica

Dear Jessica,

Your mom reminds me of a tribe of Indians known as Diggers. They did not have any weapons like bows and arrows to hunt with, so they were forced to dig for roots and eat grasshoppers. That's not my idea of a Thanksgiving dinner!

Some Diggers actually tried to hibernate during the coldest winter months when grub was scarce. In the spring, when the first blades of grass appeared, the Diggers who were still alive would crawl out of their holes and eat grass until they were strong enough to go back to digging roots.

Life in the Wild West was not kind to vegetarians. The Diggers would have killed for a triple bacon burger with cheese and extra bacon.

Get 'em while you can, girl!
Grizzly

LAKE HAVASU
DEC. 27
ARIZONA

80
80

Thanks for visiting Lake Havasu Scott Sorensen,

Everybody sure liked you. But I would say our lunch lady liked you best. Her name is Mavis. She said you were handsome and that your outfit was the coolest. I told her your outfit was made from buckskins and that you chewed on the fringes whenever you got hungry. She laughed and said she would have given you school lunch if you were that hungry. Lucky you left. We had vegetables with chicken gravy that looked like barf.

I would rather eat buckskin.

Your pal,
Homer

Howdy Homer,

You are absolutely right—a trapper could chew his buckskins in "starving times." But most mountain men could find roots, bugs and berries even in lean conditions.

When old Joe Meek was stranded in a blizzard, he had to chew the fringes off his buckskin leggings. Once the fringes were gone, he tore into a rotten tree trunk and found it full of ants. He figured he'd starve trying to pick them up one at a time. So he rubbed sap onto his palms, set his hands back into the swarming ants, and in no time at all was gulping them down by the dozens. "They taste like nuts n' honey," he said with a grin.

Your friend,
Grizzly

Dear Mountain Man,

I have watched you talk and you have very fine stories and a good speaking voice, I commend you for that. You were standing up straight and did not slouch or bite your nails. You were composed but still energetic. And your program was appropriate for 4th graders.

All in all, you have done a nice job and no one got bored like the time Miss Manners and Miss Behavior came to tell us how to wash our hands, say thank you, and not throw food so we will have esteem.

Your friend,

Amy

Well, Miss Amy,

Those are mighty nice compliments. It means a lot coming from a tough critic like yourself. It took me years to stand up straight and quit biting my nails.

Last spring I met Miss Manners and Miss Behavior at a school in Sacramento and you're right. They were boring as a bag of rocks. Although it appears you learned a thing or two from them, young lady.

Your friend,
Griz

Howdy Scott Sorensen,

Your show was great! I didn't get bored for one second even though most of it was a pack of lies.

Have you ever shot a jackalope? Probably not. They only come out once every 35 years and only at night. They have shiny green eyes, sharp horns, and only eat petrified wood. Unless they can't find some—then they eat ants. But only black ants because red ants don't taste good and will bite you. Never eat red ants. And never kick their ant hills either because they will crawl in your pants and bite you.

Your friend,

Alex

Hey Alex,

I've never shot a jacakalope, but I had one in my sights. I was ready to pull the trigger when I felt something crawling up my legs. By golly, I was standing smack dab in the middle of an ant hill! And you're right, Alex. Those pesky bugs sure can bite. That jackalope ran off laughing and left me whooping, hollering, and slapping my buckskins.

Your friend,
Grizzly

Hello Mountain Man,

Thanks for coming to my school. Do you hate school? I do.
Do you like skateboards? I do.
Do you like skateboarding in the winter? I do.
Do you like watching skateboarding videos? I do.
How many states have you been to in America? I've been to five states. I skateboarded in all five of them.

Some day I'm going to quit school and go on a skateboard trip to all 37 states.

Your friend,
Joey

p.s. Have you been to college? It doesn't seem like it.

Whoa there, Joey,

I might not be the smartest wolf in the pack, but I know which way my stick floats. And last time I checked, there were at least 39 states. We added Hawaii and Alaska a while back.

Check your atlas and stay in school, buddy.

Your friend,
Grizzly

Dear Grizzly,

One time me and my family went to Grandma's house way out in the desert.

The next morning me and my brother and sister were eating popsicles, playing in the sprinklers, and listening to music when a whole family of wild javelinas came out of the desert and chased us into the house. Then they played in our sprinklers and ate our popsicles and turned our music up way too loud.

Those javelinas stayed there all day singing and dancing and eating our popsicles. One of them even put on grandma's hat and sunglasses and drank her orange juice. Then the big ones jumped into the jacuzzi hot tub while the little ones did back flips on the trampoline. Grandma says that javelinas are really dangerous and very rude.

What do you think?

Your friend,

Derek

HOWDY, DEREK OLD HOS,

YOUR GRANDMA'S RIGHT, JAVELINAS CAN BE DANGEROUS AND THEY ACT LIKE PIGS. I WOULD RATHER HAVE A GRIZZLY BEAR IN MY HOT TUB THAN A PACK OF THOSE BRISTLY BEASTS.

AND YOU, MY FRIEND, KNOW HOW TO STRETCH THE TRUTH AND WEAVE A TALE. YOU HAVE THE MAKINGS OF A TOP-NOTCH MOUNTAIN MAN.

YOUR FRIEND,
GRIZZLY

Dear Mr. Mountain Man,

I just wanted to say thanks for your visit. I have a story to tell you.

It all started when my uncle Hal was hunting. He was loading his gun and pulled the trigger. It shot his toe off. Now he is missing his pointer toe on his right foot. It doesn't look pleasant, but it is just one of those things.

He also got stabbed in the leg with his own hunting knife, but he still loves hunting. I don't think you could ever make him hate hunting.

Your friend, Jordan

p.s. I am a female

Dear Jordan,

So uncle Hal shot his pointer toe off. Yowch!

He reminds me of a Blackfoot warrior known as Stabs-by-Mistake. He was courageous in battle but reckless when swinging his knife. In two different fights with his enemies he stabbed himself. Once in the arm and once in the leg.

Maybe that tale is some consolation for your uncle Hal. At least he's not the only person who ever wounded himself.

Happy hunting,
Grizzly

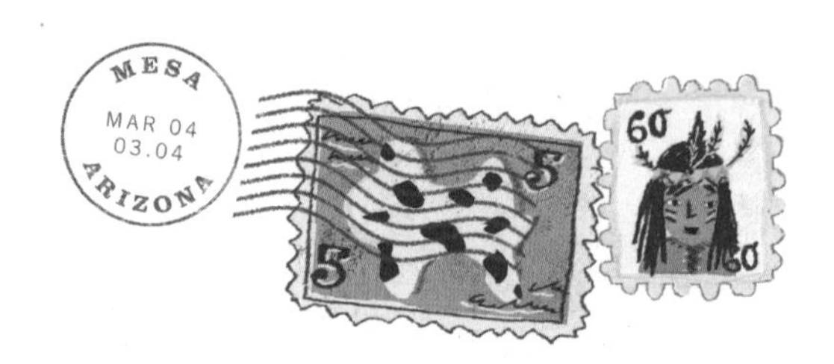

Hi Scott Sorensen,

Thanks for letting us fourth graders touch your furs. My old friend Bailey Hutchings touched your wolf skin the wrong way just like you told us not to. He touched it with the sticky side of his hand and said he would punch my face if I told on him. He don't scare me one bit. But don't tell him I told you anyway.

Your friend,

ANTHONY

p.s. Bailey Hutchings has red hair and freckles and his phone number is 369-2728.

Hey Anthony,

Thanks for the phone number. I remember that freckle-faced rascal, Bailey. He had his sticky paws all over my wolf skin, and he's in a heap o' trouble. I'm calling him first thing in the morning if I can find a phone. Last time I used one the darn thing stole my quarter.

Your friend,
Grizzly

Dear Mountain Man,

Thank you for your presence at our school. I enjoyed your show and wish you could have stayed longer.

I learned a lot about how mountain men like to make animal calls and then they come and tear you to pieces. But I don't know why mountain men like to do that? I asked my mom if I could buy one of those animal calls but she said, "No!" Because she knew that I was either going to lose it or maybe get killed by a wild beast. Or else I would play with it and give her a headache.

Well, I've got to go. I still have a long day ahead of me and I don't want to miss my bus.

Love,

Patricia

p.s. I like how you are not embarrassed to talk to kids when you are wearing those funny pants.

Dear Patricia,

Sometimes I do get embarrassed by my funny pants. But a lot of great men wore funny pants—George Washington, Christopher Columbus, Robin Hood...

Anyway, I figure I'm in good company.

Your friend,
Grizzly

Hi Mountain Man,

Thanks for a real good show. It was the best day of school in over 4 years.

I really liked the elk whistle and the wounded rabbit caller. I can make the sound of the creature called a loon. It is because I have a very high voice. My teacher said, "Enjoy it while you can Bernie because in a couple of years you will probably sound like a moose with a bad cold."

Mrs. Cameron always makes jokes like that. On the weekends she works at Harrahs State Line Casino. She knows about 100 card tricks and can make things disappear and come back again. She is my favorite teacher. My Dad says she is a perfect role model.

Your friend,

Bernie

p.s. Did you know you have a better chance of getting struck by lightning than winning the lottery? Mrs. Cameron told me that.

Hello Bernie,

Mrs. Cameron is right. I have nearly been struck by lightning three times but have never even come close to winning the lottery.

I don't gamble 'cause it gets folks into trouble. A trapper named Bill Sublette got into a gambling game with some Crow Indians that went on for two days. Bill dropped out after losing his horse and a pile of beaver pelts. But two of the Crow warriors kept playing until one of them had lost everything he owned—including his horse, rifle, knife, blankets, beaver pelts and even his moccasins. But he refused to quit. He bet his scalp against everything the other warrior had won from him, but his medicine was bad and he lost again. So he sat without complaint as the winner cut the scalp from the top of his head.

There is a lesson to be learned here, Bernie. Watch yer topknot and don't play blackjack with Mrs. Cameron. You have a better chance of being struck by lightning than beating her in a game of cards.

Your friend,

Grizzly

Dear Mr. Mountain Man,

Thanks for visiting our school. We have a blue and green parrot named Jasper in our classroom. One time when I was feeding it, Jasper bit my finger and made it bleed.

I know how to cuss in Japanese. If you don't believe me, just ask Jasper. Now he can cuss in Japanese too.

Sincerely,
Bianca

Dear Bianca,

Old Jasper sounds like a real feisty bird. The craziest critter I ever had was a cat named Ham. We brought him to our cabin to get rid of the mice, But it turned out that mice were just his appetizers. I'll be darned if that cat didn't catch frogs off the beach, chase woodchucks into the forest, and terrorize the chickens in our coop.

One night a bat came down our chimney and began flying in circles around our bedroom. Ham jumped up on the bedpost, snatched that bat out of midair and swallowed it whole.

Ham had an attitude sort of like Jasper the parrot. But I never heard him cuss in Japanese.

Sincerely,
Griz

Mountain Man,

I learned a lot from you like how they put out traps for beaver. I tried it with a mouse trap. It didn't work out. All I caught was my brother's hamster Mister Whiskers.

Your cat named Ham is very brave. He does better protection than most dogs. I know my dog wouldn't be that brave. My mom named my dog Petunia, so you know he is no tough dog. There is nothing to scare off around here anyway except maybe a cat in the backyard or a poltergeist in the garage.

Your friend,
Michael
(owner of a scaredy-cat dog)

HELLO MICHAEL,

SORRY ABOUT MISTER WHISKERS. WHAT AN UNLUCKY HAMSTER. AND YOUR SCAREDY-CAT DOG PETUNIA SOUNDS DADGUM USELESS.

HOPE YOU CAN FIGURE OUT WHAT TO DO WITH THAT POLTERGEIST. AT LEAST IT IS ONLY IN YOUR GARAGE. SO FAR.

YOUR FRIEND,
GRIZZLY

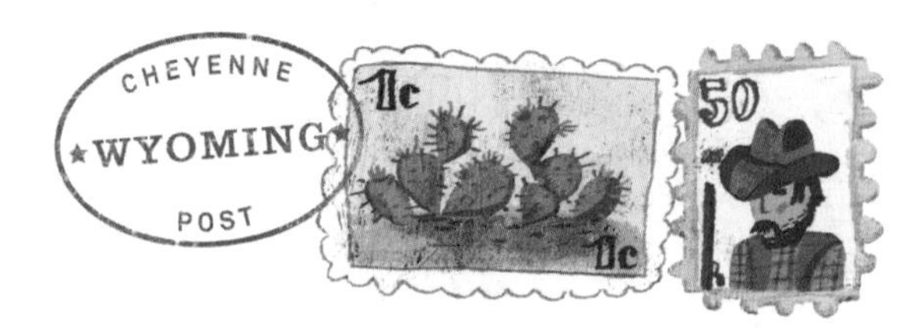

Hello Grizzly,

You are a great hunter. The only things I've shot are tin cans, water bottles, and a television from my grandpa's garage.

I am the boy on the third row with curly hair and a Spider-Man shirt. I have eczema. I wanted to show it to you but my teacher said "No" and made me sit down.

Your friend,

TAIT

Howdy Tait,

I sure would've liked to see that eczema. A trapper named Windy Bill had a case of it once. He called it "the itch" and cured it with a mixture of willow root and rattlesnake tail. He said that remedy was big medicine.

You can find willow root along any creek bed. But rattlers live under rocks in deep dark holes full of spider webs. Don't be scared, Tait. Just wear your Spider Man shirt.

Your friend,
Griz

Dear Mr. Grizzly,

Thank you for coming to our school. I had a great time. I liked when you were using all of the animal callers.

I thought the muzzle loader wasn't going to shoot. But it was loud! I think you chipped a piece off the piano when you fired your rifle. Don't worry, I put it in my pocket before Mrs. Tobler saw it. That can be a secret between me and you. If you send me an animal caller, I will probably forget it ever happened.

Your special buddy,

Oscar

Oscar, little buddy,

Thanks for covering my back. I really didn't think that old musket was loaded. And even if it was, I was aiming at the clock ABOVE the piano. Those old muzzleloaders are not very accurate.

Anyway, I'm sure glad you can keep a secret. I put your animal caller in the mail today. It is an original Primos turkey caller. From now on whenever I see a little turkey, I will think of you.

Grizzly

Hello Mountain Man,

My name is Gilda and your stories inspired me to try an experiment to see what kind of food bears like to eat.

I decided the best way to do the experiment was to have a taste test. So I took my four-year-old brother Petey into the woods and tied him to a tree with a Twinkie in one hand and a Ding Dong in the other hand. Petey began to whine like he always does. Then a black bear, a brown bear, and a polar bear came. The black bear ate the Twinkie, the brown bear ate the Ding Dong, and the polar bear ate Petey.

I hope you like my experiment.

Your friend,

Dear Gilda,

What an amazing experiment. You proved three things: black bears like Twinkies, brown bears prefer Ding Dongs, but polar bears will eat just about anything.

Keep up the clever experiments. You have the potential to be a fine scientist—if you don't run out of brothers first.

Your friend,
Grizzly

Dear Mr. Sorensen

My name is Jim and I liked when you told us that story about the bear. My question is, how old are you? My mom is 37 and she is very pretty. Her name is Tiffany. You would like her very much.

Your friend,

Jim

Dear Jim,

I am 58 years old and my wife, Mrs. Grizzly, is somewhat younger. You should see that woman throw a tomahawk and shoot a rifle. And her porcupine stew is the best in the rocky mountains.

So we best leave it at that,
Mr. Grizzly

Dear Mr. Sorensen,

One day my pet gerbil named Chip got angry and stomped out of his cage. He went straight to the Lego box and dumped them all out on the floor. Then he built himself a huge gerbil mansion with a swimming pool and a water slide. Then he went inside and called Pizza Hut and ordered two large pizzas. When those pizzas came, Chip told me to pay for them and bring him the TV by his swimming pool and turn on his favorite show called "When Animals Fight Back."

When I told my dad what happened, he took me to a therapist.

Sincerely,

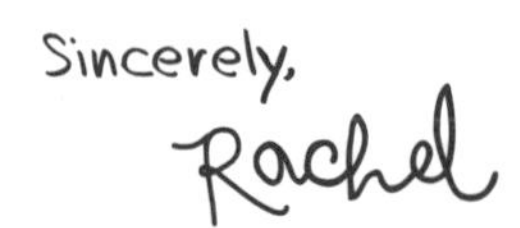

Dear Rachel,

You gotta be careful who you're spinning yarns to. I stretched the truth one too many times to Mrs. Grizzly and she took me to a therapist.

That "doctor" tried to hypnotize me by swinging a pencil in front of my eyes. Wouldn't you know it, in five minutes the therapist and Mrs. Grizzly were both sound asleep. I sat there whittling that pencil for an hour.

Turns out I paid a lot of money just so those two could take a nap.

Your friend,
Grizzly

Dear Mountain Man Sorensen,

My name is Cally. I really enjoyed the assembly you gave at our school. Last year when my family moved from Chicago to Colorado, my sister said it would be boring. But it wasn't. I would like to tell you a story that happened in my own backyard.

Once we had a neighbor who was giving a party next door. He accidentally left three glasses of wine and a cheese ball on the porch. There was a big raccoon skamming the neighborhood for food that night. The raccoon saw the wine on the porch, so he climbed up the railing and jumped on the table and drank all three glasses and ate the whole cheese ball. Then of course, he came to our house drunk and fell in the pond and threw up all over the place. Yuk!

My mom said, "Wow, there goes the neighborhood, Cally." I told my sister Colorado is not a boring place at all.

Your friend,

Cally

Hey, Cally girl,

Raccoons are notorious party animals. They will eat and drink almost anything. And leaving wine on the porch is sure to encourage rowdy behavior in raccoons.

One night a raccoon with a peanut butter jar stuck on its head came stumbling up to our campfire. I grabbed its hind legs to keep it from falling into the flames. Mrs. Grizzly took hold of the jar, and we pulled in opposite directions. The raccoon's head popped out all covered in peanut butter. I let go of the hind legs, and that critter lit out towards the tall timber.

Your friend,
Grizzly

Hey Grizzly Dude,

You are forever awesome!

My name is Cody and I am going to be a mountain man when I grow up. I have a deal for you. If you will teach me how to hunt, trap, fish, and build a log cabin, I will teach you how to yo-yo.

Your friend,

Cody

Hi Cody,

So, you are offering yo-yo lessons in exchange for a lifetime of mountain man expertise. Humph. It sounds like I'm getting the short end of the stick. I'll have to give this some thought, you little horse trader.

In the meantime, keep your eye on the skyline and your yo-yo in motion.

Happy trails,
Grizzly

Dear Mr. Mountain Man,

Thank you for your visit. My teacher is making us write letters to you. She says I have to use over half the page. Anyway, I am going to take the positive side of this. Blah blah blah

blah blah blah

blah blah

blah blah blah

blah blah

blah blah blah

blah blah blah

blah!

Your friend,

Riley

p.s. Please don't write back cause I don't want to answer your letter.

Dear Mr. Sorensen,

Hi! My name is Ramiro.

I enjoyed your presentation because you gave us a lot of facts and information for our brains. I am a worker in the Kitchen and I had to leave early, so I didn't get to see the gun shot. But I heard it. Boy oh boy, did I hear it! One lunch lady screamed and dropped her pan of Jello and said a bad word that rhymes with spit.

Only it wasn't spit. It just rhymes with spit.

Your friend,

Ramiro

HI RAMIRO,

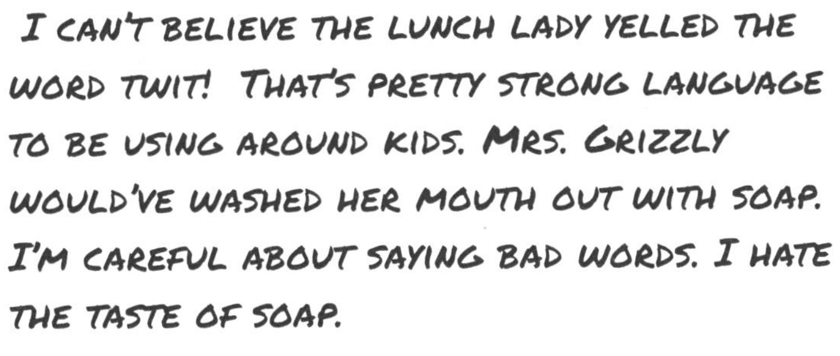
I CAN'T BELIEVE THE LUNCH LADY YELLED THE WORD TWIT! THAT'S PRETTY STRONG LANGUAGE TO BE USING AROUND KIDS. MRS. GRIZZLY WOULD'VE WASHED HER MOUTH OUT WITH SOAP. I'M CAREFUL ABOUT SAYING BAD WORDS. I HATE THE TASTE OF SOAP.

YOUR FRIEND,
GRIZZLY

Dear Mr. Sorensen

Thank you for coming to Longfellow School. Mr. Sorensen, I would like to ask you a question. How did that trapper who yelled at the bear die? Did he die temporarily or did he die permanently?

Do you like coming to schools to teach kids about the mountain men? I would like to be a mountain man, but I prefer being a pastor that preaches in church. I like going to church to learn about God. You should read the Bible everyday and pray a lot. God will always bless you where ever you are and He will take care of you from danger like if a bear attacks you. I hope to see you around some time and remember to read the Bible and say your prayers.

God bless you, Mr. Sorensen.

Sincerely,
Giovanni

Dear Giovanni,

Your letter reminds me of a very brave mountain man named Jedediah Smith. He carried a Bible in his saddlebag and offered prayers over the graves of trappers who were killed by grizzly bears and Indians.

In fact, Jedediah was torn up by a grizzly himself. The bear dragged him from his horse, broke his ribs, and ripped the ear off the side of his head. Old Jed was a sorry sight. Some of his partners started digging his grave, but Jedediah rolled over and told them to quit digging and stitch him up. They found Jed's ear laying in some brush, and sewed it back onto his head. It was a pretty rough job, but they did the best they could. Some said that his ear was sewn on upside down and too far back, but Jed didn't mind. Now he could hear critters coming from any direction, and no grizzly ever snuck up on him again.

Anyway, Giovanni, I think you would be a great mountain man or a great preacher. Or you could be both, like Jedediah Smith.

God bless you, Giovanni,

Grizzly

Dear Mr. Mountain Man,

I was so excited when I heard you were coming to our school. I loved every part. I still have goose bumps! History is the most important subject and you inspired me. When I grow up, I want to teach social studies because it is so interesting. My favorite part is learning about the trappers and explorers.

Unlike most girls, I was not sad to see those animal skins. And I was not grossed out to hear about Jedediah Smith getting his ear torn off by the grizzly bear. After all, he survived didn't he? And I loved your buckskin clothes and your bear claw necklace.

My brother Kyle is in second grade and he likes to play with Barbies. Don't worry, I will have him ready for you in two more years. His training starts today! There is no excuse for him not to be a mountain man.

Yours truly,

Becky

YOU'RE RIGHT BECKY,

HISTORY IS THE MOST IMPORTANT SUBJECT. IT TEACHES US ABOUT WHO WE ARE AND WHERE WE COME FROM. AND THAT CAN DETERMINE WHO WE WILL BECOME. I THINK YOU WILL BE A GREAT SOCIAL STUDIES TEACHER.

AS FOR KYLE, DON'T BE TOO HARD ON HIM. HE WILL FIND HIS WAY, JUST LIKE JEDEDIAH SMITH DID AFTER THAT FIGHT WITH THE BEAR.

SINCERELY,
GRIZZLY

Dear Grizzly,

Are you a real mountain man? Then where is your corncob pipe? Yesterday when you came to Roosevelt, I went home to tell my mom that a mountain man came to our school, and she said, "Did he have a corncob pipe?" I said, "He had a trap and a rifle and a possibles bag and a trade blanket and a quill pouch and a powder horn." But she said, "Did he have a corncob pipe?" I said "No, but he had a mountain lion fur and a coyote skin and a black bear rug and a badger cat." She said, "I don't think he is a real mountain man."

I wonder if there is any real mountain man?

Your friend,

Marissa

p.s. Where is your corncob pipe?

Hey Marissa,

Why is your mom so hung up on the corncob pipe? Even if I had one, I don't believe it would convince her that I am a real mountain man. Maybe she has me confused with someone from the Ozarks or the Appalachian Mountains. Has she ever heard of a hillbilly?

Your friend,
Grizzly

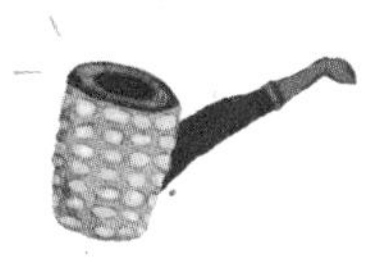

Dear Maintenance Man,

I missed your presentation yesterday because I was sick. But I heard all about it, and I think you are a fake. You're not a real maintenance man. You didn't have no tools or wrenches. I Know cause my Dad is a real maintenance man. He is a worker for the Las Vegas Valley Water District. When I grow up, I am going to be a maintenance man too. A real one.

From,

NATE

p.s. Here is my dad's favorite joke. How do you fix a broken chimp? With a monkey wrench.

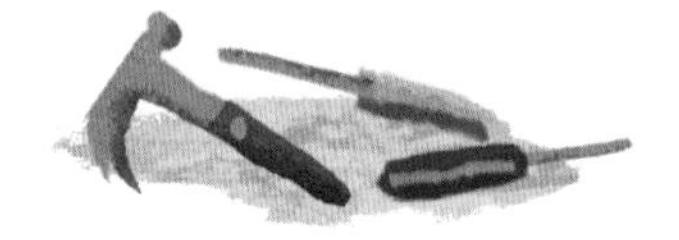

WELL CUSS ME FOR A COYOTE, NATE!

I FOOLED EVERYONE IN THE CLASS BUT YOU. I AM GLAD YOU WERE ABSENT SO NOBODY FIGURED ME OUT. IT ISN'T EASY BEING A MAINTENANCE MAN. EVEN A FAKE ONE.

YOUR FRIEND,
GRIZZLY

Hey Mountain Man,

Thank you for coming to our school. And thanks for picking the time we were supposed to do writing. I hate writing! My mom said, "There is no job that does not include writing!" But you proved her wrong. I'm going to be a mountain man too.

Now to get down to business. Can you send me one of those things you used to make the animal sounds? But I want new ones, not old ones you have licked. That's all I have to talk about.

Your Friend,
Sam

p.s. Remember to send the animal noise makers. New ones, that have never been licked.

p.s.s. Write me a sheet of paper on how to use them. Oh yeah. I forgot you don't know how to write. Okay, just draw pictures then.

Dear Sam,

Since my husband does not know how to write, I am answering this letter for him. I am also sending you an elk whistle and a goose caller. My husband licked one of them, but he would not tell me which one. And he is too lazy to draw you pictures on how to use them. But they are pretty simple. Just put them in your mouth and blow air through them. Enjoy your new animal callers. I wish he would tell me which one he licked.

Yours truly,
Mrs. Grizzly

Dear Sorensen,

Thanks for coming to Fremont School. I liked the part when you showed us the skins because it was sure interesting to see the animal skins all flattened out and torn off the creature's body.

And Sorensen, I just want to know what was the first animal you carved up? Have you ever knifed a bear in the heart? Those animal sounds you did sort of creeped me out. But Sorensen, everybody liked you so much it wouldn't bother me or anyone else if you came back again. Remember Sorensen, you are always welcome at Fremont School. So take care and please don't get killed.

Sincerely,
Cortez

p.s. I will write about you in my journal, Sorensen

Hi Cortez,

Thanks for your nice letter and warm welcome at Fremont School. Did you know that your school is named after John C. Fremont the famous western explorer? He was a man of destiny. Just like you, Cortez, he kept a good journal and made maps that encouraged thousands of pioneers to follow their dreams and go west on the Oregon Trail.

Fremont also led the Bear Flag Revolt, which helped California become part of the United States. He made a fortune in the Gold Rush, then ran for president of the country. He lost the election, but Abraham Lincoln made him a general in the Union Army during the Civil War.

Fremont's maps and journals changed the course of history. And so can yours, cortez. Keep up the good work.

Your friend,
Sorensen

Dear Mountain Man and Trapper Scott Sorenstein [sp],

Thanks a bunch for coming to our school. You brought a lot of scope for our imagination here. Usually we are in a dark box all squished up inside.

I have a question that keeps bouncing around in my head. Do you think a raccoon could steal quarters from a sock in my drawer? I have quarters stolen a lot. My brother Reese says a raccoon must be doing it. I think it is my brother Reese. Either way, what is the best way to catch them? I would really appreciate your advice on this matter.

With all due respect,

Amelia

Dear Amelia,

Ain't no way a raccoon is stealing those quarters. It's your thievin' brother Reese.

What you oughta do is catch a live raccoon and put him in that sock drawer of yours. Next time old Reese gets a hankering to snatch quarters—Whooee!! That'll teach him!

Let me know how it goes,
Grizzly

Dear Mr. Sorensen,

Thank you for coming to our school in Las Vegas. My name is Arturo but my friends call me Speedy.

I want to ask you if my class can come to visit you up there at your cabin to have some very nice adventures like yours. It's because my class hasn't done the adventures you have. I collected some data of the things you have done like fishing, hunting, kayaking, canoeing, and rock climbing.

As you can see out of 28 students:

8 have been fishing,
two have been hunting,
zero kayaking,
zero canoeing,
and 12 rock climbing.

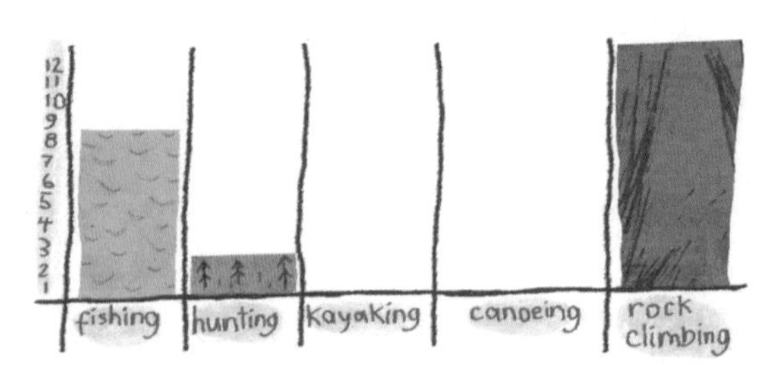

As you can see, we really need that trip.
Hope you write back soon because this is urgent!

Sincerely,
Arturo "Speedy" Hernandez

Dear Arturo,

You really deserve a trip to my cabin in the woods. It is quite different from Las Vegas, where you have world-famous attractions like Treasure Island, Caesar's Palace, Circus Circus and much, much more. Everyone wants to be in Las Vegas.

At my place in the wilderness I am surrounded by eagles, hawks, bears, wolves, Mrs. Grizzly and lots of other predators. Most folks don't even know how to find us. The more I think about it, the more I understand why you want to visit us. You really need this trip. You have to keep it a secret though, or pretty soon everyone will want to come. Then our cabin in the woods would be just like Las Vegas.

Your friend,
Grizzly

Hi Scott Sorensen,

Is it fun being a mountain man? I think it's cool because you get to be in the wilderness and have adventures.

Did you ever try to fight a bear in a dark cave? What do you do if you are all by yourself in the forest with only a knife and a bottle of whiskey? I know what my uncle Phil does. He gets drunk.

Sincerely,

Travis

Hello Travis,

There is a bird in the North Woods called a Whiskey Jack and he loves to eat elderberries off the trees near our cabin. In the fall the berries get "fermented," which means they turn into wine. One old bird got so drunk on elderberries he was staggering around our deck singing off-key and bumping into flower pots.

That bird couldn't hold his liquor any better than your uncle Phil.

Keep the cork in your bottle,
Grizzly

Dear Mr. Mountain Man,

I really liked when you came to our school. I will never forget you. I became so sad when you left. I wish I could rewind time and hear it all over again. I'm glad you got your dream come true to be a mountain man.

One day a girl went walking in the woods. Her name was Destiny. She was not afraid of the bears or the wolves or even the dark. She decided to be a mountain girl. She would like to be your daughter and go fishing and hunting and dive off a waterfall. So can she?

Please check the correct box:

☐ Yes
☐ Maybe

I hope it is yes.

Your friend, the mountain girl,

Well Destiny,

I have five daughters and each one is a mountain girl. They would be right proud to have you for a sister. I have no doubt that you could fish, hunt and dive off a waterfall. After all, your name is Destiny. And when your story is finished, there will be no finer mountain girl than you.

Your friend,
Grizzly

Dear Mr. Mountain Man,

My name is Ketch and you done a real good thing at our school today. It was the best show I ever seen.

I am glad you came cause a man on the radio said the world will end tomorrow. I don't believe him but just in case I'm not doing no homework tonight. And I'm not cleaning my room or brushing my teeth. And I'm letting my dog Rip sleep in my bed with me. What will you do if the world ends tomorrow?

Your friend,
Ketch

HEY THERE, KETCH,

DON'T YOU WORRY ABOUT THIS OLD COON. WHETHER OR NOT THE WORLD ENDS, I'M HEADING TO MY CABIN IN THE NORTH WOODS—ACROSS THE GREAT DIVIDE TO THE HIGH AND LONESOME. JUST LIKE YOU, I WANT TO LIVE WILD AND FREE AND NOT BRUSH MY TEETH. OR AS HUCK FINN SAID, "I'M GOING TO LIGHT OUT FOR THE TERRITORIES BEFORE AUNT POLLY TRIES TO CIVILIZE ME."

I GOT MY RIFLE, CANOE, FISHING POLE AND MRS. GRIZZLY ALL PACKED IN MY WAGON. WHEN I GET TO MY CABIN, I AM GOING TO CATCH A BIG FISH, STRIKE UP A FIRE AND HOWL AT THE MOON. SO KEEP YER EYE ON THE SKYLINE AND YER NOSE TO THE WIND.

YOUR FRIEND,

GRIZ

THANKS

Thanks to the thousands of students who have sent letters over the years sharing their thoughts, tall tales, and even some family secrets.

With appreciation to the dedicated teachers who enlighten the minds and spark the imaginations of our youth.

Thanks to my daughter Michelle whose eye for detail and talent for design are on every page of this book.

And with love to my wife, "Mrs. Grizzly," delightful companion in a thousand and one adventures.